D1177721

The Moon
of the
Alligators

The Thirteen Moons

The Moon
of the
Alligators

By Jean Craighead George

Illustrated by Adrina Zanazanian

Thomas Y. Crowell Company   *New York*

Two eyes poked above the still water. Each iris was silver-yellow and each pupil long and narrow. They were the eyes of the alligator of Saw Grass Hole who was hungrily watching for food. She saw the cloudless sky above her, the grasses that edged her pool, and because her eyes were to the sides and rear of her head, she could see all the way behind her to the tall cypress trees. The trees twisted like silver wire above the tangle of sweet bay and buttonbushes.

The alligator did not move, but watched and waited as hunger gnawed her belly. The new moon of October was rising, marking the beginning of Florida's dry season. The alligator had eaten little since the rainy season began in June. Since August she had been searching in desperation. Now her sense of seasonal rhythm told her that the clear skies above, the end of the rains and hurricanes, meant food. Yet nothing had come her way—not a fish, turtle, or mammal.

1

Her waters were empty. Even the birds passed over her hole.

She was in her pool in the Everglades of Florida, which is not a swamp, as the Everglades are usually called, but a river like none other in the world. It seeps south from Lake Okeechobee to the Florida Bay, is forty to sixty miles wide and one hundred miles long. Saw grass, its rugged blades edged with teeth, fills the river from shore to shore.

The river and its creatures respond to the wet and dry seasons of this semitropical world. During the summer rains, the grass stands in water a foot or two deep. Fish flash among the stalks. Crayfish, snails, and turtles hunt in the shelter of the grasses. Then winter comes and the river dries up. The sun evaporates the water; the plants take it up and release it into the air through their stems and leaves. The peat—decayed grass that forms the river's bottom—dries and cracks in the sun. Beasts leave the grasses and gather in the alligator holes or in the sloughs and buttonwood creeks. They live through the long drought in these, the only pockets of water remaining in the Everglades.

The river begins to drop when the rains end
in October. For thousands of years this was a
crucial time for the alligators as they waited for
their food to return to their ponds. In this cen-
tury, however, man has drained the glades to
farm the rich peat. Animals have died by the
millions for lack of water. Food has always been
hard to find in summer, but today, particularly
following a drought, there are so few frogs, fish,

4

turtles, and birds that the alligators often die of starvation. Only the strong survive to feed on the creatures that fill their ponds in October.

The big six-foot alligator of Saw Grass Hole did not know the reasons for her hunger—she only knew that her belly ached. She sank to the bottom of the pool to look around. A few minnows too small to catch darted beneath her. A pollywog rested in the warm mud. She swirled

5

her powerful tail and circled her home. The water was filling with algae, one-celled plants that begin to grow profusely under October's bright sun. Long strips of cells floated in scummy masses. These bothered her. For centuries the alligators have adapted to the dry season by becoming the chief caretakers of the glades. Digging their holes deeper, pulling out the weeds, they benefit themselves and all life—from the one-celled rotifer to the stately bobcat.

The alligator drove herself into a patch of algae and caught it on her nose. Swimming hard, she carried it to the shore and pushed most of it up on the bank. Then she crawled out of the water and pulled the rest out with her teeth and claws. She bulldozed another load of this tangly plant away and went to the pond lilies. Taking a stalk in her teeth, she yanked a plant from its moorings in the mud and marl and dragged it up on shore.

When she was done she could see the minnows more clearly, and the minnows, freed from the weeds, flickered back and forth across Saw Grass Hole as they sought food. For the five-year-old alligator, however, there was no food in the water, and she surfaced once more to watch for mammals and birds in the grasses and trees.

Fifteen feet deep and some forty feet long and wide, her pool was far out in the middle of the Everglades. One end sloped up to form a slide where she sunbathed. Nearby in the shallows grew the pond lilies, where the little bass hid in the winter. Close to shore stood a clump of

six-foot-tall alligator flags, bananalike plants that grow in 'gator holes. These plants announce the locations of the alligators' homes to man, bird, and beast. When the lizardlike reptiles are killed or die, the plants die too, for the hole changes. The water thickens with algae; weeds move in and choke out the flags. Finally bushes take over and close the pool.

Now, waiting in her pool, the alligator hung at the surface, her eyes and nostrils protruding like knobs on a log. She did not know it, but the shift of life to the 'gator holes was already beginning. A snowy egret suddenly alighted on a limb of the cypress tree. The bird had changed with the coming of October. He no longer held his feathers close to his body, but lifted them slightly to let his lacy plumes float like a veil. He was expressing his first feelings of love. The moon of October begins the breeding season for the egrets. They dance on tree limbs displaying their feathers, or pick up sticks.

The egret that the alligator saw dropped into the willows beneath the cypress, picked up a twig, and flew away with it—a present for his mate. His yellow feet and black legs gleamed as he skimmed over Saw Grass Hole and climbed into the air. He was headed for his rookery on an island in a buttonwood creek near the Florida Bay. The big 'gator watched him until he was out of sight, then once more went hungrily down into her pool. She swam so gracefully that no ripples stirred as she submerged to hunt. Her huge jaws were closed in a grin over seventy

10

sharp white teeth. Her tail, almost half of her, torpedoed her across the pool to the shore where the cypress grew. As she came up on land, water spilled from her sculptured armor and her eyes refocused for sight in the air. She had to eat.

A rustle beneath a pop ash alerted her, and she shoved her way into a brushy jungle that she and her ancestors had created. For a thousand years the alligators of Saw Grass Hole had tended their pond, carefully weeding it and piling the debris on the shore. Seedlings of trees had taken hold in the rich weedy compost. The trees had formed a jungle that attracted rabbits, raccoons, bobcats, and river otter. The 'gator moved toward the pop ash with surprising grace and quickness. She startled a marsh rabbit nibbling on leaves.

The rabbit had been born in the spring, and with the rise of the moon of October had left home to seek his fortune. He had not gone far before he came upon the alligator's jungle, and finding it unoccupied, he had settled in. Blackish-brown in color, he looked like a cottontail, except he had no white on his tail. However, he possessed the same ability to leap as his northern cousin. Before the alligator could lunge he had catapulted over her six-foot-long body and plunged into the pool. The marsh rabbit quickly covered the length of Saw Grass Hole and bounced ashore.

As he disappeared the alligator felt even hungrier than before. She slid into her waters, sank, and scanned the bottoms of the lily leaves. No dark dents marked the bodies of resting bullfrogs. They had not come back to her pond. She waited, the sun went down, and she remained hungry.

The next morning she crawled onto her sunny slide to warm up her muscles. Since she had no internal heating device, she depended on the sun, air, and water—whichever was warmest—to limber her up. After basking for an hour she weeded her hole, just as her ancestors had done before her. Then she pulled ashore and started off into the Everglades to look for food. The trail she followed was as old as the 'gator pool. It, too, had been made by generations of alligators of Saw Grass Hole. A raised roadbed, the trail had

been built as the 'gators walked through the grass, trampling and killing it, until it formed a ridge of peat. The path was used heavily twice a year. In April bulls came from tens of miles around to breed the females. In October, the females and young kept it open as they, like the 'gator of Saw Grass Hole, went out into the river of grass to hunt.

The alligator moved more slowly on land than
in water, yet she covered the mile to the edge of
her property long before noon. She was in haste
and knew where she was going: to her hammock.
It was one of the many islands in the Everglades
that have been given this special name. Hammocks are unlike any other islands in any other
rivers.

They are tree-enclosed greenhouses that rise gray-green above the grass-filled waters. No drying winds penetrate the leaves of the live oaks, gumbo limbo, and mahoganies that live on the islands. In this moisture grow spectacular gardens of orchids, air plants, ferns, and mosses.

The alligator climbed into the hammock. She pushed through red maples and pop ashes that grow at the hammock edges and entered a large, dimly lit room canopied with dense leaves. It was warm and humid. A bobcat was sleeping on the broad limb of a live oak above her. He did not frighten her. The alligator has no enemy but man.

She rounded a mossy log and came to a stop. Her reptile memory warned her of an old disaster. Blanketed with orchids and air plants, the live oak above her was terrifyingly familiar. The alligator lay still.

The fear passed and she walked on a few steps. Then she saw the greenish-lemon flower of October's green-fly orchid. Again she stopped. Cautiously she looked around. Beside her bloomed the snow-white ghost orchid. Even the grass ferns that draped a palm trunk like beards were familiar. The resurrection ferns on a nearby log were curled and brown to live out the dry season. They, too, reminded her of disaster. She did not want to go on.

Hunger overcame her fears. She started off again, went a few steps, and stopped. A flock of warblers dropped from the canopy where they had been feeding. They flitted over mosquito-filled air plants. The little birds were migrating from the north. On their way to the Gulf Coast and South America they paused every October

in the hammocks to fill up on insects. Groups of robins moved through the trees. They, too, were migrating, and they, too, warned the alligator.

Yet she knew she must eat. Her hungry body drove her to a hole in the center of the hammock. It was a solution hole, fifteen feet deep, leached into the soft limestone by organic acids from decaying plants. Water filled it to its mossy edge. In its depths swam huge garfish that had entered the hole through tiny cracks in the stone. They had grown too large to get out. The alligator hesitated once more. The budding airplants, the lacy ferns, the whistling warblers—all held her back from food. She had been here before.

The sun went down, and the alligator could not see. She lay still, sleeping with her eyes "open," for she had no lids to close.

The moon came up, the raccoons walked tree limbs, and the bobcat continued his solitary October trek across the glades. He had left his mother and his brother only days ago, and he would now walk alone until his breeding season in late December. Then he would leap and play with a female of his choice, mate, be driven off, and once more wander the glades alone.

22

Night and sleep calmed the alligator's hunger, but at dawn she moved closer to the solution hole. Food was below her, yet she could not take it. Animal warnings imprinted on her mind held her back. The most violent was a memory of October and the hammock. That had been a hard time, yet none of her life had been easy.

Her life had begun under a mound of vegetation near Saw Grass Hole. The mound was a nest eight to ten feet wide and five feet high that had been used and cared for by the long line of female alligators of Saw Grass Hole.

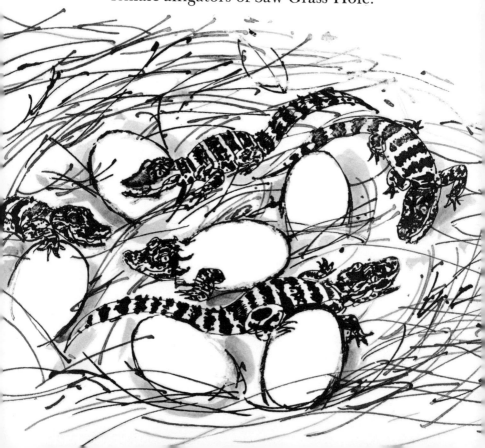

Buried in the ancestral debris when she hatched, the alligator had heard her mother above her, grunting and calling through the warm decaying plants to all her babies. The little alligator had pushed out of her brittle eggshell and struggled toward the sound. Then a great clawed foot gently pulled back the vegetation, and the baby of Saw Grass Hole scrambled into August's steamy heat.

She was joined by thirty-nine other alligators just like herself—six inches long, black, with bright yellow spots on the end of each body scale. Full of spirit, the babies began to snap at each other and run toward their grunting mother, who quickly led them down the side of the nest.

Even on that first day of life the alligator had a strong sense of survival. She marched under the protection of her mother's jaw. Her behavior was wise. No sooner had the alligators reached

the trail than a great blue heron dropped out of
the sky. He ate two babies before their mother
could swat him with her tail. Other herons and
wood storks gathered. They harassed the march-
ing group. A black snake slipped down from a
tree and swallowed a baby. A raccoon, hearing
the confusion, awoke and ran after a straggler.

When the baby alligator reached Saw Grass
Hole there were but twenty-three of the forty
left alive. Already she knew her mother meant
safety, and she entered the pond close to her
mother's side. She followed her down into the
glassy water, where bright flecks of sunlight
danced and beetles scooted past.

26

Tiny fish darted away from her. Instinctively the baby snapped at them as she traveled close to her mother into a huge cave. Not visible from the surface, the cave had been chewed, clawed, and scraped into existence by the alligators of Saw Grass Hole. It was as big as a church. The reptiles slept here at night and rested here during the cool days of winter when the chill slowed them down.

For the next nine months the baby 'gator swam out into the pool to catch minnows and bugs. She learned to avoid snapping turtles and birds, and by April grew to be eighteen inches long. She stayed with her mother until another year passed and a huge bull came to Saw Grass Hole. He swam, rolled, and splashed with her mother. He bellowed mating cries that could be heard a mile away. Then he departed and the alligator's mother was no longer friendly. She charged her two-foot daughter, and when food grew scarce in the rainy season, drove her out of Saw Grass Hole. The mother's loyalty lay with a new clutch of eggs in the ancestral nest mound.

The young alligator took the family trail through the saw grass and spent the next months near the hammock. She felt the river rise and watched the fish and turtles swim away. Then October came and the river began to dry. The alligator went into the hammock to hunt. She walked beneath the orchids and the mahogany trees. She passed the mossy log and came upon the solution hole. It was filled with trapped fish. Unhesitatingly she plunged in, and before sunset she was comfortably stuffed.

For a week she lived to her satisfaction, and then, restless to move on, she tried to climb out. She could not. The water had dropped too low; the steep sides of the solution hole were impossible to scale.

All through October she watched the live oak tree. She saw the warblers and the robins. Then the airplants bloomed and the world above her narrowed. She dropped deeper and deeper into the dark pit until only the orchid-covered oak limb was visible.

By mid-winter all the fish were gone. Starvation threatened the young alligator. One night

a marsh rabbit fell into the solution hole, and several weeks later a raccoon tumbled down to her. She existed on chance and disaster. By May the hole was completely dry and she was on the bottom, weak and hungry.

June brought back the rain. Clouds gathered, thunderstorms flashed above her, and the solution hole began to fill. One July day during a torrential storm she was floated to the top. Mustering what little energy she had left, she crawled out of her trap and slowly dragged herself home to Saw Grass Hole.

Weeds filled her pool and huge snapping turtles surfaced ominously. The alligator flags were faded. The green waters were untended, her mother gone. Like millions of other beautiful 'gators, she had been killed by poachers for her fashionable skin.

The young alligator went to work. She ate the snapping turtles and farmed the pond, pulling out weeds and algae. The fish returned, the birds came to eat the fish, and mammals came to catch the birds. When Saw Grass Hole was once more a balanced community, the alligator flags again brightened the edges with their flashy leaves.

That had been two years ago. Now the alligator was remembering the solution hole in her own way. She did not go after the fish, but lay and watched them. For three days she hung around the mossy edge of the hole, torn between her terrible hunger and her sense of survival. On the fourth day a family of raccoons approached the hole. She lunged at them, but quick and agile, they jumped onto the trunks of trees and scampered up into the canopy. One raced down the trail, and the alligator turned and followed. She was no match for him, but faced toward home, she kept on going. She wound under the red maples, out into the saw grass, and down the ancestral trail.

She slipped into her pool. Four days had changed it. The water had dropped three inches. Unweeded, the algae had choked to death as the water fell. As the plants decayed they took oxygen from the water. Many of the minnows could not breathe and had also died. Once more the alligator went to work—dragging, pushing, shoving—to clean her hole and make it livable again. Her hunger became a constant pain, but when the moon came up that night she was sleeping in her chamber, her waters sparkling from her efforts. Around her drifted little bass. They had left the glades that night, and finning their way through the inlet, had made themselves at home in the well-weeded pool.

The water dropped lower. The alligator worked on. One morning snails were abundant at the edge of Saw Grass Hole. Near the hole, the Everglades was dry, and the snails had moved to the moist edges of the pond.

Three egrets came to the pond to fish the shallows. The following afternoon five arrived, then twenty-five. They could no longer catch enough fish in the drying glades. Other birds joined them. Purple gallinules came to eat the snails and the coots arrived to eat the algae. One dawn, down the inlet swam a school of small garfish. They fed on the minnows and the water insects in the hole. The 'gator cleared more space for them and let them grow.

The leaves of the cypress fell to the ground. The alligator flags turned pale yellow. The persimmon and maple trees—northern migrants— had already colored; their leaves were ready to drop. Responding to their heredity, they remain leafless for a few weeks; then they bud and leaf and flower again. The show of October that is so brilliant in the north is hardly noticeable in Florida. Winter exists as a pause.

The herons came to Saw Grass Hole in ever

increasing numbers, while beyond the grassy
river shores farmers plowed fields and planted
cucumbers, beans, and tomatoes, in the topsy-
turvy spring of Florida's October.

The bass grew rapidly and the big white wood
storks, now beginning to nest in the rookeries
with the egrets, came to the hole to fish. Still the
'gator was hungry. None of the food she was
tending was large enough to clamp her mouth
upon.

Several big bullfrogs came to the edge of the
pond. They, too, were feeling the dryness of the
October moon. As their skins tightened they followed the smell of dampness out of the saw grass
right to the 'gator hole.

36

A crayfish that had lived all summer under the moist roots of the cypress stalked to the pond bank and began picking up clumps of marl in its claws. These it placed in a pile. Digging and scooping, it cut itself a tidy round hole to the water. Backing down, it entered Saw Grass Hole. Other crayfish joined it.

All across the glades the 'gator holes shone like glass in the crackling grass. The river was almost dry. Turtles with their backs out of water were struggling toward the holes; garfish fought their way to them, puddle by puddle; and the birds congregated around them in fluttering flocks.

A huge snapping turtle began his October trek to Saw Grass Hole. At dawn he was near the inlet. Before him a school of large garfish leaped and wriggled toward the pool.

At sunup the hungry alligator left her chamber. She moved slowly, for she was still cold from the night, but she had no time to limber up in the sun. The bass were bigger, the pond lilies growing too fast. She crossed Saw Grass Hole to weed once more. Braking midway, she turned and shot to her inlet. The huge old turtle was entering Saw Grass Hole. Flopping around him were the garfish.

The alligator moved with speed, opened her jaws, and closed them on the tasty turtle. She crunched sloppily and then plunged down upon the big gars.

In a few minutes she was full, her long fast over.

That night, when the moon of October came up, the little community in the saw grass was an oasis of life. Its keeper was in her cave, fat and full, a "smile" on her reptilian face.

ABOUT THE AUTHOR

The Thirteen Moons series has grown out of Jean Craighead George's lifelong enthusiasm for the natural world. These books reflect her special interest in ecology—particularly in phenology, the study of the relationship between climate and periodic biological events.

Mrs. George is co-author of *Dipper of Copper Creek*, which received the Aurianne Award for the most outstanding animal story published in 1957. *My Side of the Mountain, The Summer of the Falcon, Gull Number 737, Spring Comes to the Ocean, Coyote in Manhattan,* and the books in The Thirteen Moons series all have affirmed her remarkable sensitivity both to nature and to young people.

Mrs. George is a regular contributor of nature stories to *Reader's Digest.* She has held the position of art editor for *Pageant* magazine and served as a newspaper reporter for the *Washington Post* and International News Service.

ABOUT THE ILLUSTRATOR

Adrina Zanazanian was born in the old whaling town of New Bedford, Massachusetts. After moving to New York City, she attended the Art Students League and received a B.F.A. degree from Pratt Institute.

The illustrator of a number of children's books, Miss Zanazanian has also done work for toy companies and for studios specializing in packaging and design. The oil paintings she does in her spare time have been exhibited at private showings.